TEDDY
and
A Christmas Visit

KT-430-072

Snow was falling on the woodland pines,
And the bears were in their den.
"You know, I've been thinking," Teddy said,
"It's time we called on old Ben."

"It will be Christmas day tomorrow,
  And I know you will all agree,
Let's take some presents to dear old Ben,
  And help to decorate his tree."

"That's a splendid idea," Jimbo said,
    "Let's get started straightaway.
We will see how many nice presents,
    We can pile up on our sleigh."

And so off into the forest,
    Went the intrepid little bears.
Pushing and pulling their sleigh along,
    Through the woodland that was theirs.

Soon they began to collect things,
    From their friends along the way.
The squirrels gave them hazelnuts,
    Put by for a special day.

The bees said, "Here's some honeycomb,
    With Christmas greetings to dear Ben.
We often visit his garden,
    In fact, it's time we went again."

The rabbits gave them some orange pippins,
Preserved in their underground store.
And Grandma Bear gave a beautiful cake,
As they passed by her cottage door.

Toad of Toad Hall gave some nice Christmas crackers,
   With a card which began "My Dear Ben..."
Whilst Rat and Mole gave a long-playing record,
   Of the great Des O'Connor's Top Ten!

Miss Bunty Bear had knitted some socks,
    "For my very sweet and dear Ben.
I'm not sure what his size is," she blushed,
    "So I've knitted him a large ten."

Lionel Bear gave some damson wine,
    "To be consumed in moderation."
Whilst Lionel's mum gave some fairy cakes,
    "Suitable for any occasion."

They picked some mistletoe and holly,
   And decorated Bessy's hat.
Belle decorated hers with snowdrops,
   Saying, "What do you think of that?"

Teddy found some fresh wild mushrooms,
  And some rosemary and thyme.
Then coming to old Ben's cottage,
  Heard him sing a little rhyme.

"Oh lack-a-day, Oh lack-a-day,
How sweet does my garden grow.
If only I could see my friends,
Much happiness would I know."

"Here we are! Here we are!"
    Came a loud chorus from the Bears.
"Forget your worries and your woes,
    Your troubles and your cares."

With that they knocked on the great oak door,
  Which Ben opened with a smile.
"How nice to see you," said old Ben,
  "I think of you all the while."

The bears gave Ben all the gifts they had brought,
 He was delighted as can be.
"You're just in time for a freshly baked cake,
 And a nice pot of Earl Grey tea."

They decorated the Christmas tree,
    With tinsel and coloured balls.
Then hung mistletoe, holly and ivy,
    All around the cottage walls.
Very soon then old Ben's cottage,
    Was looking festive as can be.
A roaring log fire in the grate,
    And a beautiful Christmas tree.

Ben was so happy,
    That the bears had come to call,
And though he liked the presents,
    Seeing them was best of all.
And so as dusk began to fall,
    The bears said their fond farewells,
They turned and waved and headed home,
    To the sound of Christmas bells.

Content that they had brought some cheer,
    To a good and kindly bear,
They reminded each other that,
    Christmas was a time for care.